بِسْمِ اللهِ الرَّحْمٰنِ الرَّحِيمِ

Color and Learn Salah

Noorart
www.noorart.com

A Textbook and Coloring Book
by Yahiya Emerick

THIS BOOK BELONGS TO:

First printing: March 2000
Second printing: May 2002
Third printing: October 2005
Fourth printing: September 2009

Published and distributed by:
Noorart
577 Sterling Dr
Richardson, TX 75081 USA
Email: Info@noorart.com

www.noorart.com
Manufactured in the USA
ISBN:1-933269-06-5

Bismillahir Rahmanir Rahim

In the Name of Allah,
The Compassionate Source of all Mercy

Color and Learn Salah

Reading for Comprehension:

Textbooks for Today and

Tomorrow

The Islamic Arts Series

Grade Level 1 - 2

M. Shamsheer Ali Baig	Program Reviewer
Noor Saadeh	Editor (Third printing)
Reshma Baig	Editor/Congruency Specialist
Qasim Najar	Consultant/Editor
Samina Najar	Consultant
Yahiya Emerick	Author
Map design	Illustrator

Reading for Comprehension: Textbooks for Today and Tomorrow is a new effort to present
information on Islam and Muslims in a manner which is in keeping with current educational
standards. This textbook is a stand-alone coloring book, designed to teach the basic procedure of
Salah, or Muslim prayer. It contains all of the pertinent information needed for the teacher or
parent to introduce the concept and practice of Salah to the student.
This book may be used in conjunction with any of
our other Islamic studies textbooks for this grade level.

Unit 1

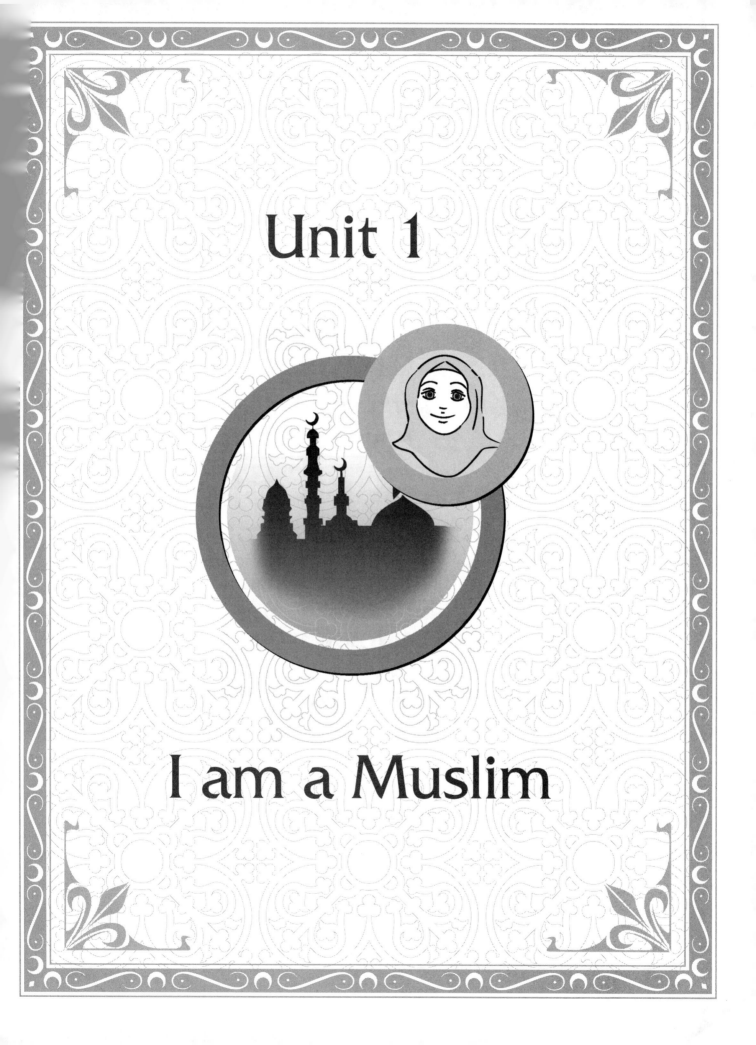

I am a Muslim

Assalamu 'alaykum. Peace be with you. My name is Fatimah.

I want to tell you about something very important.

We are Muslims.

A Muslim is a person who follows Islam.

Muslims make Salah five times every day. This is how we show Allah that we love Him.

The word Salah means Prayer.

Allah is the One Who made us and put us in this world.

This is how you write the Name of Allah in Arabic!

Allah told us in the Qur'an that we must make Salah five times a day.

The Qur'an is the book that Allah gave to us. It teaches us how to be good Muslims.

Islam is our way of life. Islam means that we listen to Allah and obey Him.

The Qur'an
is the Book of Allah

Do you know what are the five times we make Salah? They are easy to remember. We pray at these five times:

1. Before the sun comes up. This is called Fajr Salah.

2. After noon time passes. This is called Thuhr Salah.

3. Late in the afternoon. This is called 'Asr Salah.

4. Just after the sun goes down. This is called Maghrib Salah.

5. When the sky is all dark at night. This is called 'Isha Salah.

**Fajr time
is before the sun comes up!**

**Thuhr time
is after noon time passes!**

**'Asr time
is late in the afternoon!**

**Maghrib time
is after the sun goes down!**

'Isha time is when the sky is all dark at night !

Questions to Answer

Part A.

Read each word and write down what it means.

1. **Muslim:** _____
   _____
   _____

2. **Islam:** _____
   _____
   _____
   _____

3. **Allah:** _____
   _____
   _____

Part B.

Answer the questions below.

1. **Why do we make Salah?** _____
   _____
   _____
   _____

2. **What are the names of the five daily Salah?**
   A)_____ B)_____ C)_____

   D)_____ E)_____

Unit 2

I Can Make Wudu

We like going to make our Salah.
Let's hurry and get ready!

Clean is Good!

Wudu Place

We must be clean before we pray.
We wash our face, hands and feet with
water. This is called "making Wudu."

13

You start your Wudu by saying to yourself "Nuwaytul Wudu."

That means: "I am going to make Wudu." This is called making your Niyyah.

The word Niyyah means to decide to do something.

This is called
Niyyah

Then say, "Bismillahir Rahmanir Rahim."

This means, "We begin in the Name of Allah, the Most Caring and the Most Kind."

Then wash your hands in the water three times. Always wash the right side first and then the left side afterward.

If you do it right, you won't splash too much water.

Use your right hand to bring water into your mouth three times.

Rub your teeth with your finger and move it all around inside.

18

Then use your right hand to sniff water into your nose to clean it. Blow the water out hard. This is done three times for a really good cleaning.

Next, use both your hands to bring water up to your face. Pour the water all over - from the top of your forehead to under your chin. Do this three times.

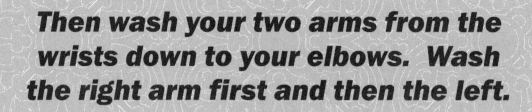

Then wash your two arms from the wrists down to your elbows. Wash the right arm first and then the left.

Don't let the water drip down off your hands. Instead, keep your hands up higher than your elbows.

Now it's time to wipe your head.
Let your fingers get wet and run
them through your hair - front to
back and then back up again.

**Wet your index fingers,
and rub your ears inside and out.**

25

The last part is important, and I know
you'll agree that the feet need
a good washing!

Wash your right foot and then your
left foot with your hands real well.
Make sure you wash between the
toes and wet your heels, too.

Now we are almost ready to make our Salah! We say a special sentence after we finish our Wudu to remind us of what we believe.

We say, "Ash hadu an laa ilaha ill'Allah, wahdahu laa sharika lah, wa ash hadu anna Muhammadan 'abduhu wa rasuluh."

That means, "I declare that there is no god besides Allah, He is One with no partners, and I declare that Muhammad is His Servant and Messenger."

This is called saying Shahadah

Next we say a special Du'a. A Du'a
is a way to talk to Allah.
This Du'a is easy. It goes like this:

We say, "Allahumma aja'alni min
at tawwabeen, wa aja'alni min
al mutatahireen."

That means, "O Allah, put me with
the people who ask for forgiveness,
and put me with the people who are
clean."

Now we are ready to begin our
Salah!

This is called making a Du'a

Questions to Answer

Part A.

Read each word and write down what it means.

1. **Wudu:** _____
   _____
   _____

2. **Du'a:** _____
   _____
   _____
   _____

Part B.

Answer the questions below.

1. **What do we say when we make our Niyyah for Wudu?**
   _____
   _____

   What does it mean?_____
   _____

2. **What are the parts of our body we wash in Wudu? Write them in order.**

   1)_____ 2)_____ 3)_____
   4)_____ 5)_____ 6)_____
   7)_____ 8)_____ 9)_____

Unit 3

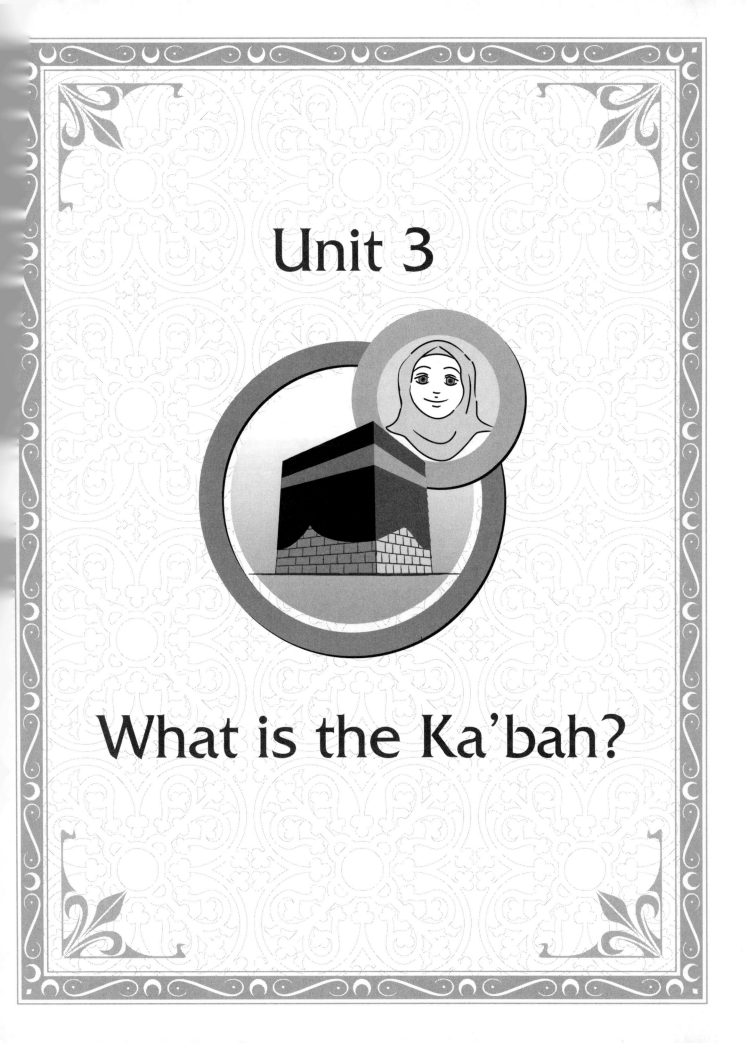

What is the Ka'bah?

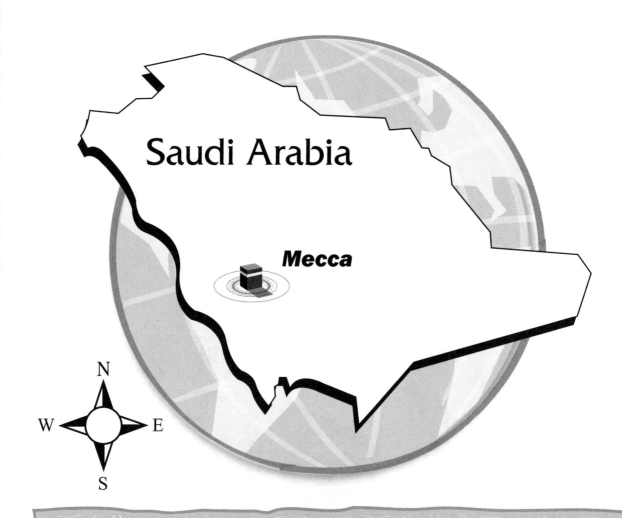

Saudi Arabia

Mecca

N
W   E
S

In the Qur'an, Allah tells us to turn towards "The Ka'bah" when we pray. The Ka'bah is the house of Allah. It is in the city of Mecca, in Saudi Arabia.

The Ka'bah is in "The Masjid Al–Haram." A masjid is a special building where Muslims pray together.

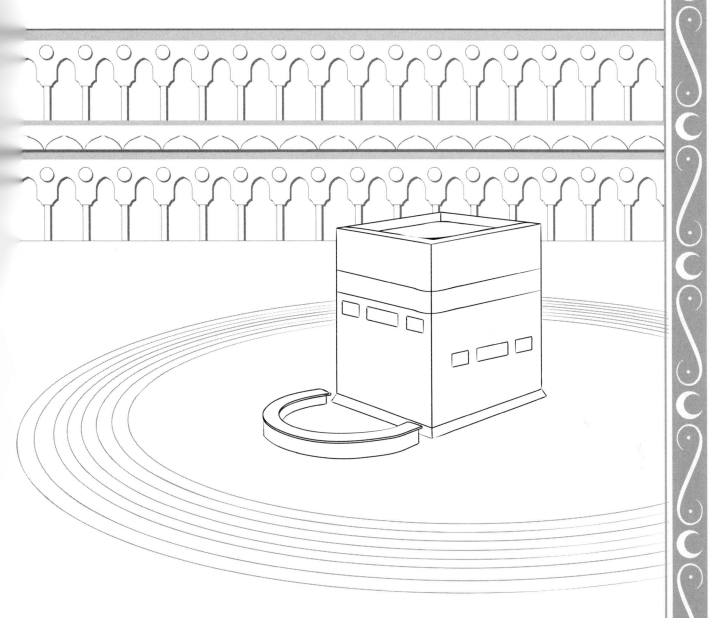

This is called
The Ka'bah

Prophet Ibrahim asked Allah to make the Ka'bah, and the city around it, a place of prayer.

So, in the Qur'an, Allah tells us to turn towards the Ka'bah when we pray. We are good Muslims and we always obey Allah.

Now, let's learn how to make Salah!

Come into our
Masjid

Questions to Answer

Part A.

Read each word and write down what it means.

1. Ka'bah:_____
_____
_____

2. Masjid:_____
_____
_____
_____

Part B.

Answer the questions below.

1. What did Prophet Ibrahim do? _____
_____
_____
_____
_____

2. Why do Muslims face towards the Ka'bah when they pray?
_____
_____
_____
_____

Unit 4

We Love to
Make Salah

Assalamu 'alaykum. My name is Rasheed, and I'll be talking to you about the Salah.

Muslims make Salah every day at least five times. This helps us to remember Allah, so we can be good.

Allah has promised to reward the good people who make Salah. He will let them into Jannah in the next life. Jannah is Paradise, or Heaven.

To begin our prayer, we stand up straight with our hands by our sides. See how Kareem and Fatimah are standing?

This is called
Qiyaam

Next, we say our Niyyah. We say, "Nuwaytu Salatul-_____" to ourselves. (We add the name of the Salah in the blank space.)

It means, "I am making the Salah of _____ now." (Add the name of the Salah in the blank space.)

Then we lift our hands up to our sides and say, "Allahu Akbar."

Those two words mean that Allah is greater than everything in the whole wide world.

Now that our Salah is started, we don't talk, laugh or move around.

This is called
Takbir

Next, we fold our hands in front of our bodies. Our right hand goes on top of our left. Then we say a small Du'a to ourselves that goes like this: "Soob hanakal lahumma wa bihamdika, wa tabaraka ismuka, wa ta'ala jedduka, wa laa ilaha ghayruka. 'Authubillahi min ash shaytanir rajeem."

That means "Glory to you Allah and praise. Blessed is Your Name and You are the Highest. There is no god but You. Allah protect us from the bad Shaytan."

This is also called Qiyaam

الفَاتِحَةُ
Al Fatihah

Next, we say Surah Al Fatihah. It is the first chapter of the Qur'an. The word Al Fatihah means The Opening. We use this Surah to open our prayers. A Surah is like a chapter.

Our Salah must be said in a language called Arabic. This way all Muslims have something in common.

Remember that Surah Al Fatihah teaches us to ask Allah for His love and help in the best words.

We say Sura Al Fatihah like this:

الفَاتِحَةُ
Al Fatihah

بسم الله الرحمن الرحيم

Bismillahir rahmanir raheem.

Al hamdulilahir rabbil 'alameen.

Ar rahmanir raheem.

Maliki yaumideen.

Eyyaka na'budu wa eyyaka nasta'een.

Ihdinas siratal mustaqeem.

Siratal latheena an 'amta 'alayhim,
Ghayril maghodoobi 'alayhim
Walad daaleen.

صدق الله العظيم

The meaning of Surah Al Fatihah is:

"In the Name of Allah, the Most Caring and the Most Kind. Praise is for Allah, the Lord of all the worlds. The Most Caring and the Most Kind and Master of the Day of Judgment."

"We serve You, and turn to You for help. Guide us on the straight path. The path of who You are happy with, not the path of who You are angry with, and not the path of who went astray."

Then we say another Surah from the Qur'an after that. Here is a short Surah called Surat Al Ikhlas.
Do you know this Surah?

الإخلاص
Surat Al Ikhlas

بسم الله الرحمن الرحيم

Bismillahir Rahmanir Raheem

Qul huwallahu ahad. ①

Allahus samad. ②

Lam yalid wa lam yulad. ③

Wa lam yakul lahu kufuwan ahad. ④

صدق الله العظيم

The Meaning of Surah Al Ikhlas is:

In the Name of Allah, the Most Caring and the Most Kind. Say that He is only one Allah. Allah the Eternal. He wasn't born, and He doesn't have any children. And there is nothing the same as Him."

After we finish saying Surah Al Fatihah, and the small Surah after that, we lift our hands up again and say, "Allahu Akbar."

Do you remember what that means?

This is called Takbir

Then we bend down and put our hands on our knees. We bow down to praise Allah. This is called making Ruku'.

We say, "Soobhana rabbee il 'atheem" three times. That means "Glory to my Great Lord."

Allah is the One Who made everything in the world and everything in the sky.

We say wonderful things about Allah because He is Great.

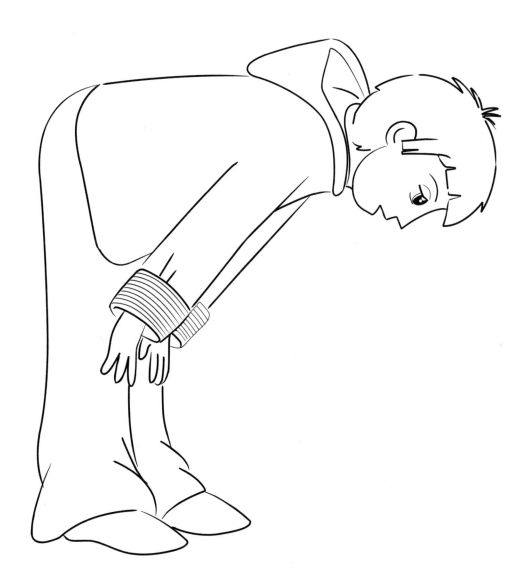

This is called Ruku'

Then we say, "Sami'Allahu leeman hamidah" and stand up straight. That means "Allah hears the people who praise Him."

Then we say, "Rabbana lakalhamd." This means "All Praise belongs to you, our Lord."

Or you can say, "Rabbana wa lakalhamd" instead, if you want to.

This is also called
Qiyaam

Now, to show Allah that we really love Him, we say, "Allahu Akbar' and then bend all the way down on the floor. This is called making Sajda.

We say, "Soobhana rabbee al a'la." three times. That means "Glory to my Highest Lord."

Be careful that your elbows don't touch the ground!

Allah loves it when we bow to Him. That is when we are closest to Allah.

This is called Sajda

Then we say, "Allahu Akbar" and sit up with our hands on our knees. Sitting like this is called Jalsa.

We ask Allah to forgive us for any bad deeds we did by saying, "Rabbee ighfirlee." That means "My Lord forgive me."

This is called Jalsa

Assalamu 'alaykum. It's me, Fatimah, again. Let me explain from here.

Say, "Allahu Akbar" and make one more Sajda, or bowing down. Now say the same words you said before. Do you remember them?

We say, "Soobhana Rabbee al a'la" three times.

This is called
Sajda

Then we say, "Allahu Akbar" and stand up straight again.

Our hands are folded in front of us. The right hand is on top of the left hand.

Here we see my friend Asma' from the back. Do you see how nicely she stands?

We just finished one Rak'a of Salah. The word Rak'a means a section or part.

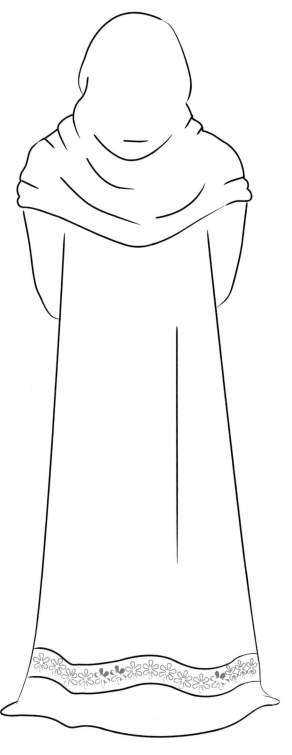

This is also called Qiyaam

Now we have one more Rak'a to do for this Salah. Every Salah has its own number of Rak'a, or parts.

We have to do all of the moves we just did all over again. Do you remember what they are?

Here they are again:

We say Surah Al Fatihah one more time and then another short Surah after it. Then we bend forward and touch our knees. Then we stand up straight. Remember to say, "Allahu Akbar!"

We bow down on the floor, sit up and bow down again. Do you remember what we say in all those moves?

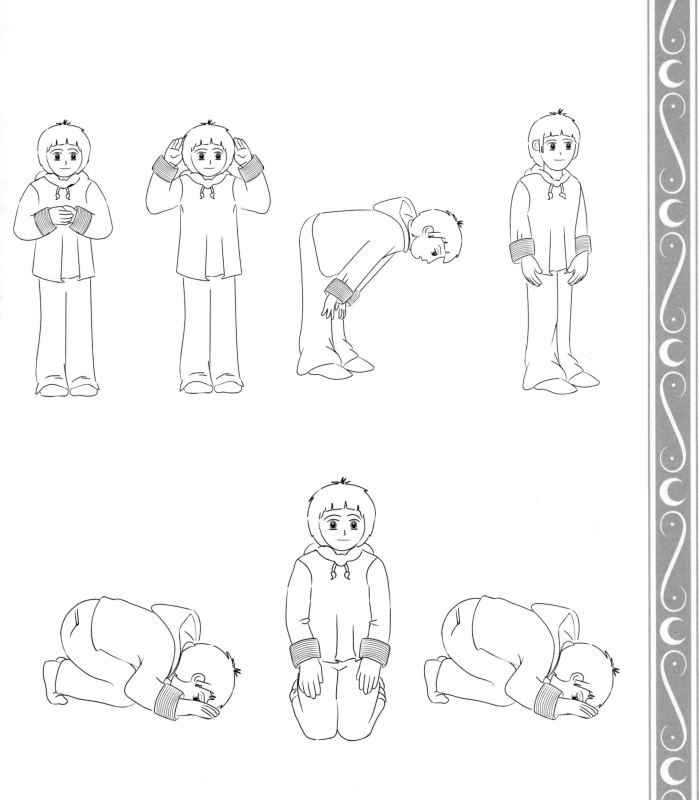

This is the Second Rak'a

Now we are ready to end our Salah. We say, "Allahu Akbar" and sit up nicely in Jalsa. Next we will say two special Du'a.

The first Du'a is a beautiful prayer where we say all of the nice things about Allah Who is the Best.

Then we ask Allah to put lots of blessings upon Prophet Muhammad, peace be upon him.

Prophet Muhammad, peace be upon him, was a great man. He came to the world to teach us about Allah.

On the next two pages you will learn these two Du'a. Once you have learned them, you will be happy.

This is called Jalsa

Keep your right foot up with your toes on the ground!

Say this Du'a:

"Atta hiyatu lillahee wa salawatu wa tayyibat. Assalamu 'alayka ayyuhan nabeeyu wa rahmatullahi wa barakatuh. Assalamu 'alayna wa 'ala 'ibadil lahis sawliheen."

"Ash hadu an laa ilaha ill'Allah, wa ash hadu anna Muhammadan 'abduhu wa rasooluh."

It means:

"All purity, prayer and goodness belong to Allah. Peace be upon you Prophet, and Allah's mercy and blessings. Peace be upon us and upon all good servants of Allah. I declare that there is no god but Allah, He is One with no partners, and I declare that Muhammad is His Servant and Messenger."

Then say this Du'a:

"Allahumma sallee 'ala Muhammadin wa 'ala aalee Muhammad. Kama sallayta 'ala Ibrahima wa 'ala aalee Ibrahim. Innaka hameedun Majeed."

"Allahumma barik 'ala Muhammadin wa 'ala aalee Muhammad. Kama barakta 'ala Ibrahima wa 'ala aalee Ibrahima fil 'alameen. Innaka hameedun majeed."

* There are other ways to say these Du'a, too!

It means:

"Allah send prayers on Muhammad and his family, just like You sent prayers on Ibrahim and his family. You are indeed the Praiseworthy and Majestic."

"Allah send blessings on Muhammad and his family, just like You sent blessings on Ibrahim and his family in the world. You are indeed the Praiseworthy and Majestic."

69

Then we turn our heads to the right and say, "Assalamu 'alaykum wa rahmatullah." That means "Peace be upon you and Allah's Mercy."

This is called Tasleem

Then we say, "Assalamu 'alaykum wa rahmatullah" to our left side.

Our Salah is now done!

Questions to Answer

Read each word and write down what it means.

1. Jannah: _____
   _____
   _____

2. Salah: _____
   _____
   _____
   _____

3. Surah: _____
   _____
   _____

Part B.

Answer the questions below.

1. What is the first Surah we say in every Rak'a?
   _____
   _____
   _____

2. What are the names of each part of the Salah?
   _____
   _____
   _____

Unit 5

Making Salah
With My
Friends and Family

It is better to make Salah with other people. Prophet Muhammad, peace be upon him, said you get more rewards from Allah if you pray together.
This is a Masjid. A Masjid is where we pray together.

This family is making Salah

Assalamu 'alaykum.
My name is Ahmad.

Here are three friends named
Fatimah,
Asma' and Maryam.

They love to make Salah together.

Making Salah together is called
Salah in Jama'ah.

This is called
Salah in Jama'ah

There is a special day called Jum'ah when all of the Muslims gather together for Salah.

They pray in the Masjid.

Everyone prays behind a leader called an Imam. Where do your parents go for Jum'ah?

This is called
Salatul Jumah

Prophet Muhammad, peace be upon him, told us that Allah is happy when we greet each other. When we greet each other we say "Assalamu alaykum" and shake hands.

He also said that if we smile at someone, Allah will reward us. Have you smiled at another person today?

This is called
Greeting
Each Other

There is a wonderful Du'a we can say to Allah after we finish our Salah. You can say it in Arabic or in English. It goes like this:

"Rabbana 'atina fid dunya hasanatan wa fil akhirati hasanatan wa qeena 'athaba naar."

It means, "Our Lord, give us the best in this life and the best in the next life and protect us from the punishment of the fire."

Say it out loud and then say, "Alhumdulillah!". This means "All Praise is for Allah!"

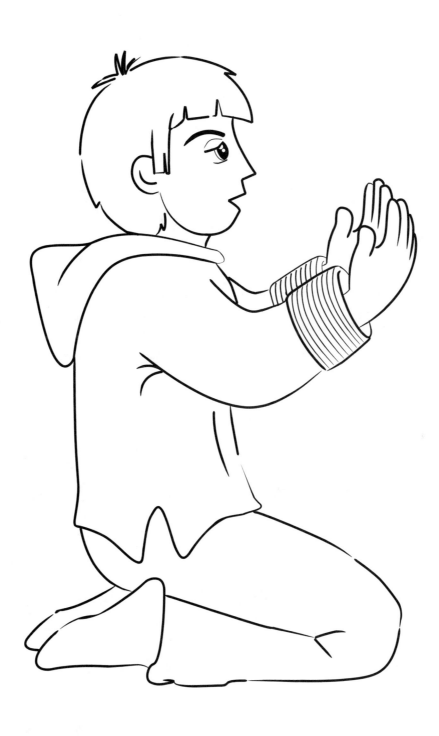

This is called
making a Du'a

In this book we learned how to make a two-Rak'a Salah.

Every Salah has its own number of Rak'a, or sections. Look at the list to the right and you will see the numbers.

Your parents or teachers can show you how to pray a Salah that has more than two rak'a.

The five Salah that we must do are called Fard Salah. The word Fard means that Allah said you must do it.

We also do other Salah to get extra rewards. Those are called Sunnah and Nafl Salah.

Salah Name	Fard	Sunnah
Al-Fajr Salah	(2) Rak'a	(2) Rak'a
Al-Thuhr Salah	(4) Rak'a	(4) Rak'a & (2) Rak'a
Al-'Asr Salah	(4) Rak'a	(2) Rak'a
Al-Maghrib Salah	(3) Rak'a	(2) Rak'a
Al-'Isha Salah	(4) Rak'a	(2) Rak'a & (3) Witr

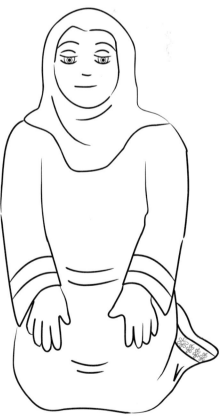

Alhumdulillah, we enjoyed learning how to make Salah with you.

Insha'llah, we will see you again. The word Insha'Allah means "if Allah lets it happen."

Remember that Allah is our God. He put us in this world so we can be good Muslims.

Making Salah helps us to be good Muslims. Prophet Muhammad, peace be upon him, always made his Salah on time.

Let's follow his example and make Salah on time, too!

Assalamu 'alaykum!
Peace be with you!

Questions to Answer

Part A.

Read each word and write down what it means.

1. Jama'ah:_____
_____
_____

2. Jum'ah:_____
_____
_____
_____

3. Insha'Allah:_____
_____

Part B.

Answer the questions below.

1. What happens on the day of Jum'ah?
_____
_____
_____
_____

2. Why is it good to make Salah with other people?
_____
_____

Draw a line to connect the words in the circles with the matching words in the squares.

Salah

'Isha

Jum'ah

Ka'bah

Night

Ibrahim

5 Times

Masjid

Part D.

Fill in the missing word on the lines in each sentence. The words you will need to use are listed here.

Words to Use:
Islam, Allah, Fard, 'Asr, Muslim, Sajda, Du'a, Qur'an

1. A _____ follows Islam and obeys Allah.
2. When we bow on the floor it is called_____
3. The Holy_____ is our book. We learn from it.
4. Salah is a _____ for all Muslims.
5. We say a _____ after we make Wudu.
6. _____ made all of us and is watching us.
7. The Salah named Maghrib comes after _____ Salah.
8. _____ is our way of life.

89

> Diverse & High Quality Products for Everyone.

> Up to 8 Inner Pages for Every Book.

> Secure & Friendly Site.

10% Discount
On Any Order Above $70

(Online orders only. See website for complete details. Code #951753)

15% Discount
On Any Order Above $100

(Online orders only. See website for complete details. Code #852654)

Noorart
www.noorart.com

Please Visit Our Showroom in Dallas TX

Up to 25% OFF for Islamic Centers and Schools